Piano Step by Step

A Series for Young and Perennially Young Pianists

Performance Pieces • Dances • Studies • Pieces for Piano Duet

An Introduction to Style

Each volume is arranged progressively ranging from easy to medium

Eine Reihe für junge und ewig junge Pianisten

Vortragsstücke • Tänze • Etüden • Vierhändiges Spiel

Einführung in den Stil

Jeder Band ist progressiv geordnet von leicht zu mittelschwer

Une série pour jeunes et éternellement jeunes pianistes

Pièces d'exécution • Danses • Etudes • Jeu à quatre mains

Initiation au style

Chaque volume est ordonné progressivement du facile au moyen difficile

Editor of the series

Herausgeberin der Reihe

Rédactrice de la serie

Ágnes Lakos

Doppelband

Johann Sebastian Bach

(Seiten 6 bis 63)

Joseph Haydn

(Seiten 65 bis 150)

K 300 & K 241

Johann Sebastian Bach
(1685–1750)

37 Piano Pieces

Compiled and provided with fingering by
Ausgewählt und mit Fingersatz versehen von
Choisis et doigtés par

Ágnes Lakos

INDEX

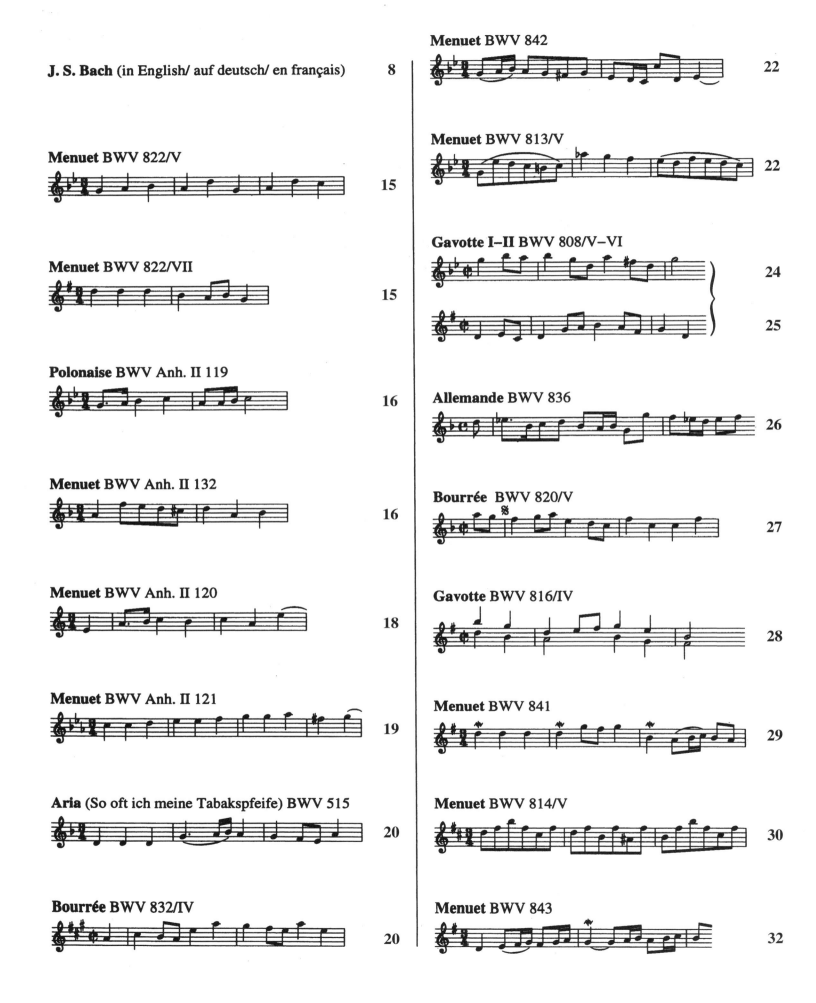

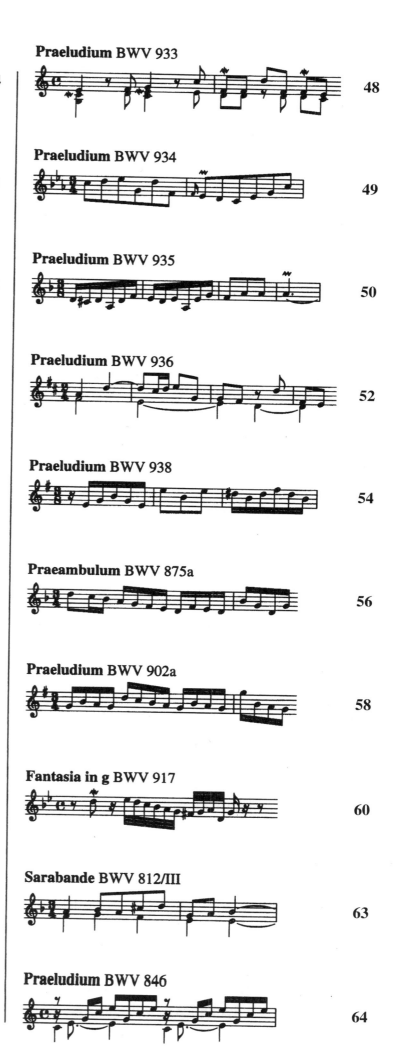

Johann Sebastian Bach

The Clavier at the Time of Bach

During Bach's lifetime in the first half of the 18th century, composers rarely stipulated which keyboard instrument should be used to perform pieces for the piano, as we would call them today. Even the mention of the word "cembalo" in the title of a sonata did not necessarily mean that a work could only be played on this instrument. One useful clue as to the instrument used was the inclusion of a pedal stop. This naturally suggested that the composition was to be played on an organ – or possibly not, as there were also harpsichords and pianos with pedals on which suitable pieces could be performed! The main keyboard instrument of the 18th century was the cembalo or harpsichord which from 1770 onwards was gradually superseded by the pianoforte. The clavichord was also extremely popular during this century. Contemporaries called these instruments claviers (from the Latin clavis or key), a collective term which could be used to denote the organ, pianoforte or harpsichord.

The clavier player had to select his instrument in accordance with the environment in which he was performing. The clavichord, for example, could only be used under certain conditions. It is by far the quietest and weakest of all the keyboard instruments; its sound carries only a few feet, thus making it unsuitable for concert performances. It was, however, ideal for intimate music-making in the home, for the private, secluded dialog between player and instrument. It also has one major advantage over the harpsichord; the volume can be varied depending on how hard the keys are struck, enabling the performer to use dynamics as with the pianoforte. This is made possible by the instrument's simple mechanism. At the far end of each key there is what is known as a tangent which hits the clavichord strings. Even after the key has been struck the string and key are still touching, allowing the player to use a special vibrato or tremolo not possible on any other keyboard instrument. This feature of the clavichord enables music to performed in a *cantabile*, singing style. Johann Sebastian Bach speaks of this "*cantabile* method of playing" in the foreword to his two-part inventions. The clavichord was probably his preferred teaching instrument as it not only demanded that the player coax his instrument to "sing" but also that he develop a delicate attack. The pieces in the *Clavierbüchlein* composed for son Wilhelm Friedemann, the inventions and the first part of the *Well-Tempered Klavier* were all used by Bach as teaching material and were thus probably written for the clavichord. The specific instrument is, however, not stipulated; as already mentioned, this was not common practice in the 18th century.

Bach the Teacher

Johann Sebastian Bach was not only one of the greatest composers in history and one of the most significant clavier virtuosi of his day and age but also a brilliant teacher of music. He taught during his entire lifetime, passing on his wisdom not only to his musical sons and daughters but to an entire host of youngsters, many of whom later became famous musicians in their own right. His pupils fully appreciated the excellence of Bach's tuition; they knew it would be almost impossible to find a better teacher of the art of keyboard playing (harpsichord and organ) and composition anywhere else. The personality and the music of the cantor of St Thomas's invariably made a lasting impression on all who came into contact with them. To have been a pupil of Bach's was a privilege which played a central role in the later careers of many of his scholars.

Johann Sebastian Bach offered his students fundamental training in counterpoint. His protégés were taught to develop a strictness of style, to think and play in independent lines and to master the figured bass. Some of Bach's best-known pieces for harpsichord are the result of his instruction at the keyboard. The title page of the *Well-Tempered Klavier*, for example, claims that the works are "for the use and application of musical youths wishing to learn". It is known that Bach even wrote down some of his harpsichord pieces during lessons.

Times soon changed, however. It cannot be denied that from 1730/1740 onwards Bach's style gradually went out of fashion. In the minds of the public, the baroque had been usurped by the *style galant* and sentimentality, by a desire for simplicity, ease and the subjective expression of emotions in music. Thus those who studied the rather passé style of composition under Johann Sebastian Bach learned what was to become the epitome of musical erudition. In the second half of the 18th century, Johann Ludwig Krebs and Johann Philipp Kirnberger, Friedemann Bach and Gottfried August Homilius, plus numerous others, were to guarantee the continuance of Bach's strict contrapuntal style and great tradition.

Bach's Virtuosity

At the time of Bach, the virtuosity of a musician was rather different to what we understand by it today. It was not merely the faultless rendition of a work, the perfect quality of the sound. To be a virtuoso a musician had to be master of his entire trade, able to conjure up a piece of music in a form which was both scholarly and demanding. The interpretation of a work was not as rigidly separated from the process of composition as it is now. A virtuoso had to be a maestro of improvisation, either following a given musical theme or freely indulging his imagination; he must, however, never disregard the rules learned during years of training! The most erudite musicians – Johann Sebastian Bach among them – even improvised in the strict "bound" style. Moments of inspiration produced highly complex polyphonic forms, such as the fugue and ricercare. 18th-century admirers of virtuosi lauded the musicians' skills of both interpretation and composition.

Musically, Johann Sebastian Bach could do anything. He played magnificent fantasias on the harpsichord. A concert he gave in Dresden in 1717 caused his rival Louis Marchand such consternation that the Frenchman disappeared from the auditorium without a trace, terrified of having to pit his musical wits against the genius of his adversary. Even in his later years Bach was a phenomenon at the cembalo. When at the age of 62 he visited the king of Prussia, Frederick the Great, in Potsdam in 1747, he amazed the royal court with his improvisation on a theme supplied by the monarch himself, taking the melody through an impromptu series of polyphonic forms. His contemporaries told each other legendary tales about his organ playing. Bach's virtuoso treatment of the pedal was his particular forte, but then Johann Sebastian Bach was a man of fortes; he had an outstanding memory, incredible powers of deduction and an unbridled imagination. To us today, these extraordinary abilities seem nothing short of a God-given miracle – much as they must have done when the great composer was alive.

Johann Sebastian Bach

Das „Clavier" zur Zeit Bachs

Die Zeit Bachs, also die erste Hälfte des 18. Jahrhunderts, legte in den wenigsten Fällen genau fest, mit welchem Tasteninstrument ein Klavier-Stück, wie wir heute sagen würden, auszuführen war. Selbst das Auftauchen des Begriffs „Cembalo" im Titel einer Sonate mußte nicht zwangsläufig bedeuten, daß das Stück nur auf diesem Instrument gespielt werden konnte. Einen Anhaltspunkt bietet in jedem Fall das Vorhandensein einer Pedalstimme. Sie macht natürlich die Ausführung des betreffenden Stücks mit Orgel wahrscheinlich, doch gab es auch Cembali oder Klaviere mit Pedalen, auf denen entsprechende Werke aufgeführt werden konnten! Das wichtigste Tasteninstrument des 18. Jahrhunderts war das Cembalo, das erst nach 1770 vom Hammerklavier langsam abgelöst wurde. Während des ganzen Jahrhunderts erfreute sich auch das Clavichord großer Beliebtheit. Alle diese Instrumente wurden von den Zeitgenossen als „Claviere" bezeichnet (von lateinisch „clavis" = Schlüssel), ein Oberbegriff, der eine Orgel ebenso wie ein Hammerklavier oder ein Cembalo meinen konnte.

Die Wahl des richtigen Instruments durch den Spieler hing vor allem von den Aufführungsbedingungen ab. Das Clavichord z. B. konnte nur unter ganz bestimmten Voraussetzungen eingesetzt werden. Es ist das bei weitem leiseste und tonschwächste aller „Claviere". Sein Ton kann nur im Abstand von wenigen Metern überhaupt wahrgenommen werden. Damit schied das Clavichord als Konzertinstrument von vornherein aus. Es war vielmehr das rechte Medium für intime Hausmusik, für das private, zurückgezogene Zwiegespräch des Spielers mit seinem Instrument. Gegenüber dem Cembalo bietet es einen gravierenden Vorteil: Es ermöglicht die Variation der Lautstärke durch die Stärke des Anschlags, also ein dynamisches Spiel, wie das Hammerklavier. Dies wird durch die simple Mechanik des Clavichords gewährleistet. Auf dem hinteren Tastenende befindet sich die sogenannte Tangente, die direkt auf die Saite stößt. Selbst nach dem Anschlagen besteht noch Kontakt zwischen Saite und Taste, so daß sogar ein Vibrato, die sogenannte „Bebung", möglich ist, die kein anderes Tasteninstrument bieten kann. Auf diese Weise erlaubt das Clavichord einen kantablen, „singenden" Vortragsstil. Eine solche „cantable Art im Spielen" spricht Bach im Vorwort zu seinen zweistimmigen Inventionen an. Wahrscheinlich war das Clavichord sein bevorzugtes Unterrichtsinstrument, da es neben einem gesanglichen Vortrag eine besondere Delikatesse des Anschlags erforderte. Die Stücke des „Clavierbüchleins" für seinen Sohn Wilhelm Friedemann, die Inventionen, der erste Teil des „Wohltemperierten Claviers" – all dies wurde von Bach als Unterrichtsmaterial verwendet und ist daher wahrscheinlich Musik für das Clavichord. Doch es existiert natürlich keine exakte Zuschreibung an ein bestimmtes Instrument, da dies, wie gesagt, nicht üblich war.

Bach, der Lehrer

Bach war nicht nur einer der größten Komponisten der Geschichte und einer der bedeutendsten „Clavier"-Virtuosen seiner Zeit, sondern auch ein genialer Musikpädagoge. Er unterrichtete während seines ganzen Lebens: Vor allem natürlich seine musikbegabten Söhne und Töchter, daneben aber auch eine Schar anderer junger Leute, die später meist auch bedeutende Musiker wurden. Alle seine Schüler wußten um die hohe Qualität des Bachschen Unterrichts. Im Spiel der Tasteninstrumente (Cembalo, Orgel) und in der Wissenschaft von der Komposition konnten sie schwerlich einen besseren Lehrer finden. Nicht umsonst spielt das Prädikat, ein Schüler Bachs gewesen zu sein, in den beruflichen Karrieren vieler von Bachs Schülern eine zentrale Rolle. Und auch die Person und das Werk des Thomaskantors hinterließen in der Regel einen bleibenden Eindruck. Bach legte den Akzent auf eine solide kontrapunktische Ausbildung. Der strenge Stil, das Denken und Spielen in selbständigen Stimmen und darüber hinaus die Beherrschung des Generalbasses wurde den Schülern vermittelt. Einige der bekannten Cembalostücke Bachs verdanken ihre Entstehung unmittelbar dem Unterricht. Nicht umsonst heißt es auf dem Titelblatt des „Wohltemperierten Claviers": „ . . . zum Nutzen und Gebrauch der Lehrbegierigen Musicalischen Jugend". Es ist überliefert, daß Bach manche Cembalostücke im Unterricht selbst niederschrieb. Und doch läßt sich nicht leugnen, daß Bachs Stil nach 1730/40 langsam aus der Mode kam. Der Galante Stil und die Empfindsamkeit, das Streben nach unkomplizierter Leichtigkeit und subjektivem Gefühlsausdruck in der Musik, verdrängten den Barockstil im Bewußtsein des Publikums. Wer also bei Bach noch nach dem alten Geschmack studierte, eignete sich gleichzeitig etwas an, das bald darauf zum Inbegriff musikalischer Gelehrsamkeit wurde. Johann Ludwig Krebs und Johann Philipp Kirnberger, Friedemann Bach und Gottfried August Homilius und wie seine zahlreichen Schüler noch hießen, sie alle waren in der zweiten Jahrhunderthälfte Garanten des strengen, kontrapunktischen Stils und einer großen Tradition.

Bachs Virtuosität

Die Virtuosität eines Musikers bedeutete zur Zeit Bachs etwas anderes als heutzutage. Das Virtuosentum wurde nicht auf eine vollkommene und makellose Wiedergabe eines Werkes, quasi auf die perfekte Qualität des „Sounds" beschränkt. Ein Virtuose zu sein bedeutete die vollkommene Beherrschung seines Handwerks, d. h. man mußte die Musik in gleichzeitig möglichst gelehrter und anspruchsvoller Form hervorzaubern können. Die Interpretation ist noch nicht so strikt vom Porzeß des Komponierens abgegrenzt worden wie heute. Ein Virtuose mußte hervorragend improvisieren können: Entweder nach einem gegebenen musikalischen Thema oder frei, nach der unbeschränkten Fantasie – aber niemals an den erlernten Regeln vorbei! Die gelehrtesten Musiker – zu denen auch Bach gehörte – improvisierten sogar im strengen, „gebundenen" Stil. So entstanden in inspirierten Augenblicken hochkomplizierte mehrstimmige Formen, wie die Fuge und das Ricercar. Wenn man im 18. Jahrhundert einen Virtuosen bewunderte, dann bedeutete das: Man huldigte gleichzeitig seinem interpretatorischen und kompositorischen Können. Johann Sebastian Bach konnte alles. Er spielte auf dem Cembalo fabelhafte Fantasien. Sein Konzert 1717 in Dresden verursachte bei seinem Rivalen, dem Franzosen Louis Marchand, einen solchen Schock, daß er vor lauter Angst vor einem Kräftemessen mit Bach in Nacht und Nebel das Weite suchte. Noch im hohen Alter war Bach am Cembalo eine glänzende Erscheinung. Als er 62-jährig 1747 den preußischen König, Friedrich den Großen, in Potsdam besuchte, setzte er den Hof mit seiner Improvisation auf ein vom König selbst gegebenes Thema in Erstaunen, das er nach verschiedenen polyphonen Arten aus dem Stegreif bearbeitete. Die Zeitgenossen erzählten sich Legenden über sein Orgelspiel. Besonders die virtuose Behandlung des Pedals war Bachs Stärke. Aber eigentlich hatte Johann Sebastian Bach nur Stärken: Ein phänomenales Gedächtnis, hohe Kombinationsgabe und natürlich unbegrenzten Einfallsreichtum. Heute wie damals mußten diese Fähigkeiten wie ein gottgegebenes Wunder erscheinen.

Johann Sebastian Bach

Le «Clavier» du temps de Bach

Du temps de Bach, c'est-à-dire dans la première moitié du XVIIIe siècle, on ne précisait que très rarement sur quel instrument à clavier il convenait de jouer ce que nous appellerions une œuvre pour piano. La mention même du terme de «clavecin» dans le titre d'une sonate ne signifiait pas toujours qu'il fallait obligatoirement jouer la pièce en question sur cet instrument. La présence d'une partie de pédalier pourrait évidemment plaider en faveur de l'orgue. Mais il existait également des clavecins ou des pianos à pédalier sur lesquels il était possible de jouer ces œuvres ! Le principal instrument à clavier du XVIIIe siècle était le clavecin, que le pianoforte n'a commencé à supplanter qu'après 1770. Le clavicorde a également connu une grande popularité tout au long du siècle. À l'époque, on appelait tous ces instruments «claviers» (du latin «clavis» = clé), un terme générique qui pouvait désigner aussi bien un orgue qu'un pianoforte ou un clavecin.

Les conditions d'exécution dictaient généralement le choix de l'instrument. Le clavicorde n'était ainsi adapté qu'à un environnement bien particulier. Cet instrument est de loin le plus doux et le moins sonore de tous les «claviers». Il ne résonne en effet qu'à une distance de quelques mètres à peine. Cette caractéristique le disqualifiait donc d'emblée comme instrument de concert. Il se prêtait bien davantage à la pratique domestique, au dialogue intime et retiré de l'interprète avec son instrument. Le clavicorde présentait au demeurant un avantage majeur par rapport au clavecin: son intensité sonore varie en fonction de la force du toucher, produisant un jeu dynamique, à l'instar de celui du pianoforte. Cet atout est dû au mécanisme très simple du clavicorde. L'extrémité postérieure des touches est en effet munie de ce qu'on appelle la «tangente», une languette métallique qui vient toucher la corde. Le contact entre la corde et la touche persiste après l'attaque, ce qui autorise même un effet de «vibrato», le fameux «Bebung» ou «balancement», dont tous les autres instruments à clavier sont privés. Le clavicorde se prête ainsi à un style d'interprétation «cantabile», chantant. Dans la préface à ses Inventions à deux voix, Bach évoque du reste cet «art du jeu cantabile». Sans doute le clavicorde était-il son instrument d'enseignement privilégié car, parallèlement à cette interprétation chantante, il imposait une délicatesse de toucher bien particulière. Les pièces du «Clavierbüchlein» destiné à son fils Wilhelm Friedemann, les Inventions, la première partie du «Clavier bien tempéré» — toutes ces œuvres lui servaient de matériel pédagogique et ont probablement été écrites pour le clavicorde. Mais il n'existe bien sûr aucune attribution incontestable à un instrument précis. Ce n'était en effet pas l'usage, comme nous l'avons dit plus haut.

L'activité pédagogique de Bach

Jean Sébastien Bach n'a pas seulement été l'un des plus grands compositeurs de l'histoire et l'un des plus importants virtuoses du «clavier» de son temps. C'était aussi un pédagogue de génie. Il a enseigné toute sa vie durant: d'abord, bien sûr, à ses fils et à ses filles doués pour la musique, mais également à de nombreux autres jeunes gens, dont la plupart sont devenus des musiciens de renom. Tous ses élèves étaient parfaitement conscients de la grande valeur de l'enseignement qu'il dispensait. Ils auraient difficilement pu trouver meilleur maître touchant la pratique des instruments à clavier (clavecin, orgue) et la science de la composition. Le titre d'ancien élève de Bach a du reste été une précieuse carte de visite dans la carrière professionnelle d'un grand nombre de ses disciples. Par ailleurs, ceux-ci ont généralement été profondément marqués par la personnalité et par l'œuvre du Cantor de saint-Thomas. Bach insistait sur la solidité de l'apprentissage du contrepoint. Il transmettait à ses élèves la rigueur stylistique, il leur apprenait à penser et à jouer en voix indépendantes et leur inculquait la maîtrise de la basse continue. Certaines de ses célèbres pièces pour clavecin ont été composées à des fins exclusivement pédagogiques. La page de titre du «Clavier bien tempéré» porte d'ailleurs cette mention: «…Au profit et à l'usage de la jeunesse musicale avide de savoir». On sait que Bach a écrit certaines de ses pièces pour clavecin au cours même des leçons qu'il dispensait. Son style commença pourtant à passer de mode après 1730/1740. La faveur du public se tourna vers le style galant, qui répondait mieux à son goût pour la sensibilité, pour la légèreté et pour la subjectivité de l'expression du sentiment musical. Le style baroque appartenait désormais au passé. Les musiciens qui continuaient à étudier selon le goût ancien auprès de Bach assimilaient ainsi un enseignement qui devint rapidement l'incarnation de l'érudition musicale. Dans la deuxième moitié du siècle, Johann Ludwig Krebs et Johann Philipp Kirnberger, Friedemann Bach et Gottfried August Homilius ainsi que tous les autres élèves du vieux Cantor allaient être les garants d'un style contrapuntique rigoureux et d'une noble tradition.

La virtuosité de Bach

Du temps de Bach, le concept de virtuosité musicale recouvrait une réalité un peu différente de celle d'aujourd'hui. La virtuosité ne se résumait pas à la restitution irréprochable d'une œuvre, ni à la qualité parfaite du son. Pour être considéré comme un virtuose, il fallait maîtriser son métier à la perfection, c'est-à-dire être capable de faire naître la musique avec une science de grande tenue et sous une forme répondant aux plus hautes exigences. Interprétation et composition n'étaient pas encore deux processus clairement délimités. Un virtuose devait savoir improviser à merveille sur un thème musical donné, ou librement, en lâchant la bride à son imagination – mais sans jamais déroger aux règles en vigueur! Les musiciens les plus savants – dont Bach faisait indéniablement partie – étaient même capables d'improviser dans un style rigoureux, «lié». C'est ainsi que des instants d'inspiration suprême donnèrent naissance à des formes polyphoniques extrêmement complexes, comme la fugue et le ricercar. Au XVIIIe siècle, lorsqu'on admirait un virtuose, on rendait hommage tout à la fois à ses compétences d'interprète et de compositeur. Jean Sébastien Bach était passé maître dans ces deux arts. Il jouait au clavecin de prodigieuses Fantaisies. Le concert qu'il donna à Dresde en 1717 troubla si profondément son rival, le Français Louis Marchand, que de peur de devoir se mesurer à Bach, celui-ci préféra s'esquiver à la faveur de la nuit. Bach resta un claveciniste brillant même à un âge avancé. En 1747 – il avait alors 62 ans –, il se rendit à Potsdam à l'invitation du roi de Prusse, Frédéric le Grand. Il plongea la cour dans la stupeur en improvisant sur un thème proposé par le roi, qu'il déclina au pied levé sous plusieurs formes polyphoniques. Sa maîtrise de l'orgue était également légendaire et l'un de ses principaux points forts était, nous dit-on, l'utilisation du pédalier. À vrai dire, Bach n'avait que des points forts : une mémoire phénoménale, un don remarquable pour la conception d'ensemble et, bien sûr, une imagination sans bornes. Aujourd'hui comme alors, ces facultés font véritablement figure de miracle divin.

Menuet

Fine

Da Capo al Fine

Menuet

K 300

Polonaise

Menuet

BWV Anh. II 132

Menuet

Menuet

BWV Anh. II 121

Aria (So oft ich meine Tabakspfeife)   BWV 515

Bourrée   BWV 832/IV

K 300

Menuet

Menuet

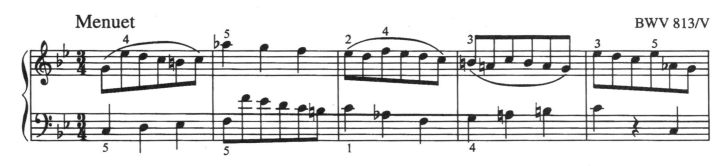

K 300

Gavotte I

Gavotte II ou la Musette

(Gavotte I Da Capo)

K 300

Allemande

BWV 836

Bourrée

BWV 820/V

Dal Segno % al Fine

Gavotte

28

Menuet

BWV 841

Menuet

BWV 814/V

Trio

Menuet da Capo

Menuet

K 300

Praeludium

BWV 939

Praeludium

Praeludium

BWV 941

K 300

Praeludium

Praeludium

K 300

Inventio in C

K 300

Inventio in F

K 300

Praeludium

Praeambulum

Praeambulum

* Fingering by the author – Fingersatz vom Komponisten – Doigté par l'auteur

46

K 300

Praeludium

Praeludium

BWV 934

Praeludium

Praeludium

Praeludium

BWV 938

Praeambulum

BWV 875a

Praeludium

BWV 902a

K 300

Fantasia in g

62

Sarabande

BWV 812/III

Praeludium

Joseph Haydn
(1732-1809)

23 Piano Pieces

Compiled and provided with fingering by
Ausgewählt und mit Fingersatz versehen von
Choisis et doigtés par

Ágnes Lakos

INDEX

Haydn

Haydn, a Professional Between Two Musical Periods

When Joseph Haydn was born in 1732 the two giants of the music world were Bach and Händel; when he died in 1809 the two names at the top were his and Beethoven's. Mozart had been dead for eighteen years. His lifetime saw the demise of the old social system, saw excited, agitated crowds destroy the Bastille, Paris' symbol of tyranny, saw people expect Napoleon to give them freedom and equality, only to receive military aggression and reinstatement of the monarchy. Hope was exchanged for disappointment in politics, Classical perfection for Romantic openness in the arts, rationalism for sensitivity in patterns of thought. Throughout these turbulent times Haydn composed unperturbed, true to his purpose and professionalism. We imagine Haydn to have been a master of the art of music. He composed regularly at the order of his patron; he received commissions and fulfilled wishes; he served specific groups of contemporary music consumers and knew exactly what kind of music he had to produce to satisfy the refined palate of a dozen or so guests at court or the desire for sensation of a thousand bourgeois concert-goers. What is quite astounding is that from 1780 onwards he dictated the musical fashion at a place which can only be found on the map with a powerful pair of glasses: Esterháza.

A Genius in Courtly Residence

Although Haydn demonstrated extraordinary musical talent at an early age, heralding him a child prodigy – to follow current convention – is perhaps a little exaggerated. He was in fact something of a late starter; he didn't take up his first permanent position until he was twenty-nine and composed his major works at an age neither Mozart nor Schubert lived to see. He had a very modest background, growing up one of many children in the eastern part of Austria (in Rohrau), until at the age of five his beautiful voice and musicality earned him a placement as choirboy first in Hainburg and then at St. Stephen's in Vienna. After his voice broke he was forced to earn a living as a freelance composer and musician. He did this for ten difficult years, without a secure livelihood, until he was appointed Hofkapellmeister to the Esterházy family. Haydn worked for the Esterházys for thirty years, the first ten years little more than a servant. Today we would say that Haydn managed the musical services with full responsibility at Schloss Esterházy in Eisenstadt, then at the wonderful summer residence of Esterháza Castle (modelled on Versailles) on the Neusiedler See. His provider was an educated aristocrat who appreciated the arts; Prince Nikolaus, with a foible for splendour, attached great importance to having at his palace art and music which would be recognised by the outside world. This it was; on one visit Empress Maria Theresa announced that if she wished to see a good performance of an opera she would come to Esterháza. The castle had an opera house, a marionette theatre and numerous artists on the staff and stood in an area which at the time Haydn signed his contract with the Esterházys (1761) was still a morass, a paradise for waterfowl.

Isolation and Charisma

For a composer, Esterháza was without a doubt not the most suitable of venues. Yet this isolation had a very positive effect on Haydn; in his artistic solitude he was free to experiment, unencumbered by popular musical trends. He wanted and was able to be original. In his workshop the symphony and the string quartet blossomed and his first masterpieces were penned in these genres. He composed many operas, various sacred works, pieces for special occasions and also a large quantity (125) of chamber music for an instrument which was considered old-fashioned even then but which his employer loved to play: the baryton.

Haydn, Composer for the Piano

Besides his other works Haydn also composed pieces for the keyboard, first writing for the harpsichord and then for the new fortepiano, the forerunner of our modern piano. He was not a virtuoso at the keyboard although he had spent time in Vienna earning his keep as an accompanist. His first biographer, Georg August Griesinger, writes that his first works were sonatinas for the harpsichord "... which he sold cheaply to his female pupils ... and minuets, allemandes and waltzes for balls". Haydn was thus familiar enough with the instrument to produce pleasant, inspired and often difficult compositions: divertimenti, sonatas, variations, various dances, in total almost 100 pieces! In this field he also knew what he had to compose for whom. In those days composers still took into account the differing skills of the experts (i.e. the professionals) and of aficionados (i.e. amateurs). Haydn had learnt this from the 18th century's main treatise on the art of keyboard playing, from C. P. E. Bach's *Versuch über die wahre Art das Clavier zu spielen* (1753, 1762), which Haydn valued very highly for a number of reasons. Haydn may not have been the born pianistic composer, unlike his honoured contemporaries Mozart and Beethoven, but without his influence Beethoven's first sonatas, for example, (dedicated to Haydn) wouldn't have been written. Today it's a pleasure to rediscover Haydn's music for the piano, an oeuvre which almost faded into oblivion during the first few decades. Haydn captures the hearts of all pianists great and small.

Haydn the Star Composer

He probably had the greatest career in music history. Very few composers started their musical lives so modestly and rose to such heights of fame and recognition as Haydn. After working at the court of Esterháza for thirty years the great man, almost sixty, ventured out to London, the freshest centre of music in his contemporary world, armed with a musical undertaking which ended in triumph; his twelve London Symphonies made him a star. When he returned home, Austria celebrated him as the greatest composer of the nation, a role Haydn happily played. He composed Austria's national anthem and two great oratorios (*The Creation* and *The Seasons*) which immortalised the most important events in people's lives and appealed to the entire population. Towards the end of his life, the nameless choirboy, the poor, exploited Viennese musician, the hermit on the Neusiedler See and London's star composer became the musical father of a nation. The pious old man thanked God every day for his fortune.

Haydn

Haydn: Der Meister zwischen zwei Epochen

Als Joseph Haydn 1732 geboren wurde, befand sich die Barockepoche mit ihren größten Meistern Bach und Händel auf dem Höhepunkt, und als er 1809 starb, war außer ihm Beethoven der bedeutendste Komponist. Mozart war bereits seit 18 Jahren tot. Inzwischen war das alte Gesellschaftssystem brüchig geworden, eine aufgeregte und aufgehetzte Menge hatte die Bastille, das Symbol der Tyrannei in Paris, gestürmt, Napoleon hatte statt der erwarteten Freiheit und Gleichheit militärische Aggression und kaiserliche Restauration gebracht. In der Politik wechselten Hoffnungen und Enttäuschungen einander ab, in der Kunst klassische Vollendung und romantische Öffnung, im menschlichen Denken Rationalismus und Empfindsamkeit. In diesem wechselhaften Zeitalter bildet Haydns Verständnis von seinem Beruf eine unerschütterliche Konstante. Wie für fast alle seiner komponierenden Zeitgenossen war die Musik für ihn zuerst Handwerk. Er schuf seine Werke zumeist auf fürstlichen Befehl: Er erhielt Aufträge und erfüllte Wünsche, bediente den Geschmack der aristokratischen Auftraggeber und wußte genau, wie er sein höfisches Publikum und die bürgerlichen Konzertbesucher zufriedenstellen konnte. Und was am erstaunlichsten ist: Ab ca. 1780 diktierte er die Musikmode von einem Ort aus, den man auf der Landkarte nur mit starker Brille zu finden vermag – vom Schloß des Fürsten Esterházy in Eisenstadt.

Ein Genie im höfischen Dienst

Obwohl Haydn sich sehr früh durch sein außerordentliches musikalisches Talent auszeichnete und die zur Übertreibung neigende Werbeindustrie ihn heutzutage als "Wunderkind" anpreisen würde, war er doch in seinem Beruf ein Spätentwickler: Er trat seine erste feste Stellung mit 29 Jahren an und komponierte seine Meisterwerke in einem Alter, das Mozart und Schubert gar nicht mehr erlebten. Haydn stammte aus sehr bescheidenen Verhältnissen, wuchs bis zu seinem sechsten Lebensjahr mit vielen Geschwistern im östlichen Teil Österreichs, im Dorf Rohrau auf, und wurde wegen seiner schönen Gesangstimme und hohen Musikalität Sängerknabe zuerst in Hainburg, dann am Wiener Stephansdom. Nach dem Stimmbruch war er gezwungen, sich als freischaffender Komponist und Musiker selbst zu erhalten. Bis ihn die Familie Esterházy an ihren Hof engagierte, mußte er zehn schwere Jahre ohne gesicherte Existenz überstehen. Haydn blieb 30 Jahre lang in ihrem Dienst, was für lange Zeit die berufliche Stellung eines besseren Lakaien bedeutete. Heute würden wir sagen, er leitete in eigener Verantwortung den musikalischen Hofdienst in Schloß Esterházy in Eisenstadt sowie im nach dem Vorbild von Versailles erbauten Lustschloß Esterháza am Neusiedler See. Sein Brotherr, der prachtliebende Fürst Nikolaus, war ein aufgeklärter, kunstsinniger Aristokrat, der großen Wert auf ein anspruchsvolles Kunst- und Musikleben in seiner Residenz legte. Anläßlich eines Besuches äußerte selbst die Kaiserin Maria Theresia einmal anerkennend, wenn sie einer guten Opernaufführung beizuwohnen wünschte, würde sie nach Esterháza fahren. Es gab ein Opernhaus und ein Marionettentheater samt dem dazugehörigen Künstlerpersonal, und dies alles in einer Gegend, die noch zur Zeit des Dienstantritts Haydns bei der Familie Esterházy (1761) ein morastiges Paradies für Wasservögel war.

Isolation und Ausstrahlung

Für einen ambitionierten Komponisten war Esterháza ohne Zweifel nicht gerade der geeignetste Ort. Die Isolation wirkte jedoch sehr positiv auf Haydn: In seiner schöpferischen Zurückgezogenheit, frei von den Zwängen der Modeströmungen, konnte er unverbindlich experimentieren. Er durfte und wollte originell sein. In seiner Werkstatt feilte er an den Gattungen von Symphonie und Streichquartett und etablierte auf diesem Gebiet mit zahlreichen Meisterwerken die klassischen Formen. Er komponierte Opern, das gesamte Spektrum der geistlichen Musik und Gelegenheitswerke, wie z.B. 125 Trios für ein schon damals altmodisches Streichinstrument, das Baryton, dessen leidenschaftlicher Spieler der Fürst war.

Haydn:
Ein Komponist auch von Klavierwerken

Nebenbei komponierte Haydn auch Musik für Tasteninstrumente, vor allem für das Cembalo, später aber auch für das immer stärker in Gebrauch kommende Hammerklavier, den direkten Vorläufer unseres modernen Klaviers. Haydn selbst war kein Virtuose auf dem Klavier, obwohl er in Wien in seiner Jugend eine Zeit lang sein Geld als Klavierbegleiter verdiente. Bei seinem ersten Biographen, Georg August Griesinger, lesen wir, daß seine ersten Werke Sonatinen für Cembalo waren, "die er zu einem geringen Preis an seine Schülerinnen verkaufte", sowie "Menuette, Allemanden und Walzer für Redouten". Haydn kannte also auch dieses Instrument gut genug, um gefällige, inspirierte und teilweise sehr anspruchsvolle Kompositionen zu schreiben (Divertimenti, Sonaten, Variationen, verschiedene Tänze – insgesamt fast 100 Werke!) Er wußte auch auf diesem Gebiet ganz genau, für wen und was er komponieren mußte. Damals wurden die Fähigkeiten der "Kenner" (d.h. der vollausgebildeten Musiker) und der "Liebhaber" (d.h. der Amateure) noch fein unterschieden. In C. Ph. E. Bachs "Versuch über die wahre Art das Clavier zu spielen" (2 Teile: 1753, 1762), übrigens der wichtigsten theoretischen Abhandlung über das Klavierspiel im 18. Jahrhundert, wird diese Unterscheidung getroffen, Haydn schätzte diese Schrift auch aus anderen Gründen sehr hoch ein. Zwar war Haydn nicht der Komponist, der vor allem die Klaviervirtuosen bedachte, doch wären die Sonaten Beethovens ohne seinen Einfluß nicht zustandegekommen – immerhin widmete Beethoven die ersten reifen Klaviersonaten seinem Lehrer Haydn. Heutzutage wird das in der Vergangenheit unterbewertete Klavierschaffen Haydns langsam wiederentdeckt und sowohl von kleinen als auch großen Pianisten immer häufiger gespielt.

Haydn, der gefeierte Komponist

Haydn hat die vielleicht größte Karriere in der Musikgeschichte gemacht. Selten begann ein Komponist seine Laufbahn so bescheiden und endete so anerkannt und in ganz Europa gefeiert wie er. Nach 30 Jahren Dienst in der musikalischen Provinz wagte er fast sechzigjährig den Sprung in die modernste Musikmetropole der damaligen Welt, London. Sein Konzertunternehmen dort war ein voller Erfolg, und nicht zuletzt seine berühmten 12 Londoner Symphonien haben aus ihm einen "Star" gemacht. Als er in seine Heimat zurückkehrte, empfing man ihn als den größten Komponisten der Nation, eine Rolle, die er gerne übernahm. Er krönte sein Lebenswerk mit den zwei großen Oratorien "Die Schöpfung" und "Die Jahreszeiten", die ihn im ganzen Volk populär machten. Der namenlose Sängerknabe, der um seine Existenz kämpfende arme Wiener Musiker, der Eremit am Neusiedler See und die Londoner Berühmtheit – an seinem Lebensabend wurde Haydn der musikalische Vater einer Nation. Der fromme Greis hat dafür tagtäglich seinem Gott Dank gesagt.

Haydn

Haydn : un professionnel entre deux époques

Quand naquit Joseph Haydn, en 1732, les géants du monde de la musique s'appelaient Bach et Haendel. Quand il mourut, en 1809, il n'avait d'autre égal que Beethoven. Mozart était mort depuis dix-huit ans. Entretemps, l'ancienne société s'était effondrée, à Paris une foule furieuse et ameutée avait pris la Bastille, symbole de la tyrannie, on attendait de Napoléon liberté et égalité, il leur substituait bellicisme et restauration impériale. Espoirs et déceptions alternaient en politique, l'art oscillait entre perfection classique et ouverture romantique, la pensée entre rationalisme et sentimentalité. En cette époque de tous les changements, Haydn composait, imperturbable, fidèle à un professionnalisme bien ciblé. Haydn nous apparaît comme un maître de l'art artisanal. Il composait régulièrement, sur ordre de son duc : il recevait des commandes et exauçait des souhaits, il s'adressait à des catégories précises parmi les consommateurs de musique et il savait très exactement ce qui correspondait au goût raffiné de quelques douzaines d'auditeurs aristocratiques, ou au besoin de sensation éprouvé par quelques milliers de bourgeois, amateurs de concerts. Et le plus étonnant, c'est qu'à partir de 1780, il dicta la mode de la musique à partir d'un lieu introuvable sur la carte, sauf à l'aide de fortes lunettes : Esterháza.

Un génie au palais d'été

Bien que Haydn se fût distingué très tôt par son extraordinaire talent musical – la publicité d'aujourd'hui, encline à l'exagération, le qualifierait d'«enfant prodige» –, il eut cependant une maturité tardive : il ne trouva de poste permanent qu'à vingt-neuf ans et il composa ses œuvres importantes à un âge que Mozart et Schubert n'ont jamais atteint. Il était issu d'un milieu social très modeste et fut élevé jusqu'à l'âge de six ans parmi de nombreux frères et sœurs, dans la partie orientale de l'Autriche (à Rohrau). Puis, comme il avait une jolie voix et qu'on le devinait musicien, il devint «Sängerknabe» à la maîtrise de Hainburg tout d'abord, puis à la cathédrale St. Etienne de Vienne. Lorsque sa voix mua, il dut gagner sa vie comme exécutant et compositeur. Suivirent dix années difficiles, sans moyens réguliers d'existence, jusqu'à ce que la famille Esterházy l'engageât comme Kapellmeister. Haydn demeura trente ans au service du prince. Cela signifie que pendant les dix premières années, il fit réellement partie de la domesticité. Nous dirions aujourd'hui qu'il dirigeait, avec entière responsabilité, l'administration et la composition des concerts, d'abord au château Esterházy à Eisenstadt, puis dans le merveilleux palais d'été construit sur le modèle de Versailles, «Esterháza», au bord du lac de Neusiedl. Son protecteur était un aristocrate éclairé et ouvert à l'art, le fastueux duc Nicolas, qui tenait énormément à mener dans sa résidence une vie ostensiblement ouverte à l'art et la musique. L'impératrice Marie-Thérèse déclara même, lors d'une visite, que lorsqu'elle voudrait assister à une bonne représentation d'opéra, elle se rendrait à Esterháza. Il y avait un théâtre pour l'opéra et un pour les marionnettes, une nombreuse troupe d'artistes, et ce dans une région qui, au moment où fut signé le contrat entre Haydn et la famille Esterházy (1761), était encore un marais, paradis des oiseaux aquatiques.

Isolement et rayonnement

Pour un compositeur, Esterháza n'était sans doute pas le lieu idéal. Toutefois, l'isolement eut un effet très positif sur Haydn; dans sa solitude artistique, à l'écart des courants de la mode, il pouvait se livrer en toute liberté à ses expérimentations. Il voulait et devait être original. Dans son atelier, fleurissaient la symphonie classique et le quatuor à cordes, et il écrivit, dans ces deux genres, des chefs-d'œuvre. Il composa de nombreux opéras, de la musique spirituelle et des pièces de circonstance, de même 125 Trios d'œuvres de musique de chambre pour un instrument à cordes déjà démodé à l'époque, le baryton, une sorte de basse de gambe, dont le duc lui-même était un joueur passionné.

Les œuvres pour clavier

Accessoirement, Haydn composait aussi des œuvres pour instrument à touches, d'abord pour clavecin, plus tard pour le pianoforte à la mode, le prédécesseur immédiat du piano. Il n'était pas un virtuose du clavier, bien qu'il eût gagné son misérable pain un certain temps, à Vienne, comme accompagnateur. Son premier biographe, Georg August Griesinger, nous révèle que les œuvres de ses débuts furent précisément des sonatines pour clavecin, «qu'il vendait à un prix modique à ses élèves», de même que des menuets, des allemandes et des valses pour redoutes. Haydn connaissait donc cet instrument assez bien pour écrire des morceaux de complaisance, inspirés et parfois difficiles («divertimenti», sonates, variations, danses diverses – presque cent pièces en tout). Dans ce domaine aussi, il savait exactement ce qu'il devait composer, et pour qui. En ce temps-là, on avait encore de la considération pour les facultés des connaisseurs (c'est à dire des professionnels) et des amateurs. C'était ce que nous enseigne le livre écrit par Carl Philipp Emanuel Bach, l'ouvrage le plus important du XVIIIe siècle sur la technique du clavier: «Essai sur la vraie manière de jouer des instruments à clavier» (1753, 1762), que Haydn estimait très haut, pour d'autres raisons aussi. Certes, Haydn n'était pas un compositeur-né pour piano, comme les plus grands de ses contemporains dignes de lui, Mozart et Beethoven. Pourtant, les premières sonates de Beethoven (qui sont précisément dédiées à Haydn) ne seraient pas nées sans l'influence de Haydn. Aujourd'hui, on découvre volontiers l'œuvre pour clavier de Haydn, restée dans l'ombre pendant les premières décennies. Haydn conquiert aussi bien les petits pianistes que les grands.

Haydn, compositeur vedette

C'est lui qui a peut-être fait la plus grande carrière de toute l'histoire de la musique. Rarement, un compositeur a commencé sa carrière aussi obscurément que Haydn, pour la terminer avec une célébrité aussi indiscutée. Après trente années de service dans un palais d'été, il osa, à presque soixante ans, faire son entrée sur la scène musicale alors la plus moderne du monde, à Londres, où impresario lui propose un contrat. L'entreprise s'acheva sur un triomphe, les douze *Symphonies «Londoniennes»* ont fait de Haydn une vedette. Quand il revint au pays natal, il fut accueilli en Autriche comme le plus grand compositeur de la nation, et il endossa ce rôle avec plaisir: il composa l'hymne impérial et deux grands oratorios (*la Création, les Saison*), qui célébraient les événements les plus importants de la vie humaine et s'adressaient au peuple tout entier. Le «Sängerknabe» anonyme, le pauvre musicien domestique, l'ermite du lac Neusiedl et le compositeur vedette de Londres, devint au soir de sa vie le père musicien d'une nation. Le pieux vieillard en remerciait son Dieu chaque jour.

3 Menuette

Hob. XV:38/II

1.

Da Capo il Minuet

2.

K 241

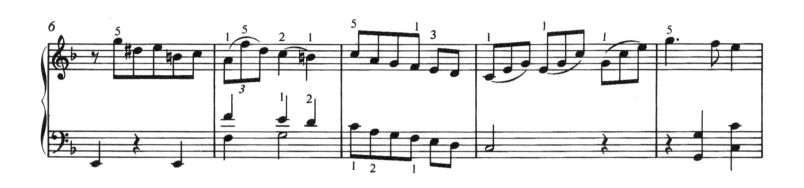

Trio

Da Capo il Minuet

3.

Trio

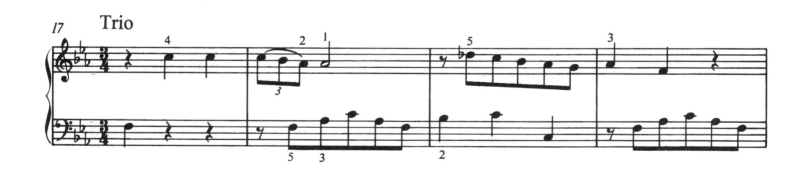

Da Capo il Minuet

2 Sonaten

Divertimento

Allegro

1.

Menuet

Divertimento

Allegro moderato

Hob. XVI:7

2.

Menuet

Trio

Menuet da Capo

Finale

Allegro

Allegretto

Kontretanz

Hob. XXXIc:17b

Allegretto

Hob. III:41/IV

Rondo

Andante allegretto

Hob. I:85/II

K 241

Andante

96

Adagio

K 241

Menuetto

Hob. I:85/III

100

K 241

Trio

Andante

102

K 241

Allegretto

6 Sonaten

Divertimento

Allegro

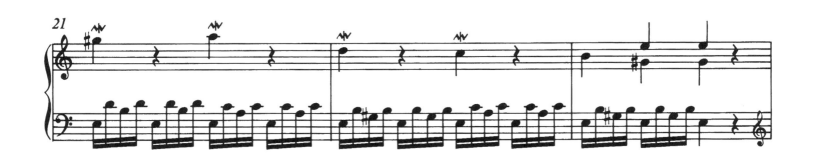

K 241

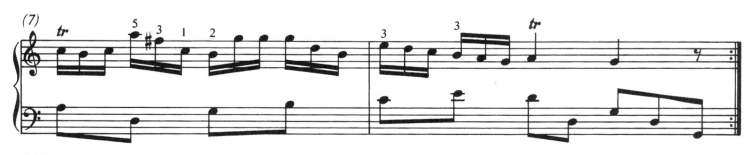

110

K 241

Menuetto

Menuet da Capo

K 241

Divertimento

Hob. XVI:4

K 241

Menuetto da Capo

Divertimento

Hob. XVI:G1

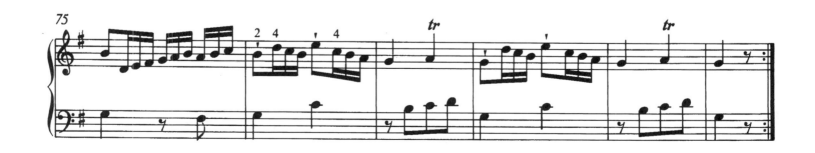

Menuetto

Menuetto da Capo

Finale

Presto

Da Capo al Segno

Divertimento

Allegro

Hob. XVI:9

4.

Menuet

Menuet da Capo

Scherzo

Divertimento

Moderato

Hob. XVI:10

5.

K 241

Menuet

Trio

Menuet da Capo

K 241

Finale
Presto

130

K 241

Sonate
Thema

Var. I

6.

Hob. XVII:D1

132

K 241

Var. II

Var. III

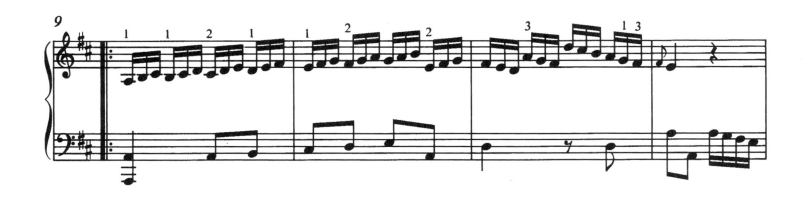

Menuet

Finale

K 241

5 Variationen in D

Hob. XVII:7

Thema

Var. I

Var. II

Var. V

12 Variationen in A

Hob. XVII:2

Thema

Var. I

K 241

Var. II

Var. V

K 241

Var. VI

Var. VII

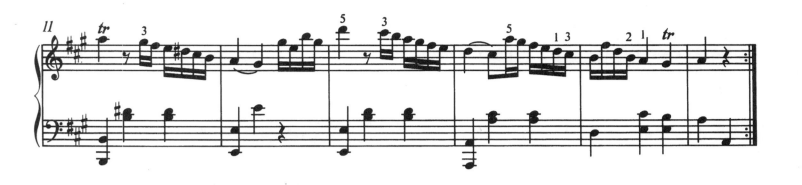

Var. VIII

148

Var. XI

Authorized special edition for Tandem Verlag GmbH
h.f.ullmann is an imprint of Tandem Verlag GmbH

© for this edition KNK GmbH, István Máriássy, and Tamás Zászkaliczky

Printed in Austria

ISBN 978-3-8331-4718-0

10 9 8 7 6 5 4 3 2 1